This edition published by Parragon Books Ltd in 2016

Parragon Books Ltd
Chartist House
15–17 Trim Street
Bath BA1 1HA, UK
www.parragon.com

ISBN 978-1-4748-5066-7

Printed in China

FAIRY TALES

PaRragon

Bath • New York • Cologne • Melbourne • Delhi
Hong Kong • Shenzhen • Singapore

Contents

The Ugly Duckling

One sunny summer day, a mother duck built her nest among the reeds near the moat of an old castle. There she laid her eggs, and there she sat, keeping them warm, day after day.

Finally, the eggs began to crack. *Peep! Peep!* Out popped each fuzzy little duckling's head, one after another.

Then Mother Duck noticed that one last egg, the biggest one of all, had not yet hatched. She carried on sitting on it. Days later, the biggest egg began to crack.

"*Honk! Honk!*" said the duckling. He was much bigger and scruffier than the other ducklings.

"He's not as pretty as my other babies," Mother Duck said to herself. "But I'll look after him, just the same."

The next morning, Mother Duck took all her babies for their first swimming lesson. They followed her into the water, one by one. They all swam beautifully – and the big, ugly duckling swam best of all!

The other ducks came to watch.

"Who's that scruffy creature?" squawked one.

"He's my youngest duckling," said Mother Duck. "See how well he swims!"

"But he's so big and so *ugly!*" quacked the other ducks, laughing.

That afternoon, Mother Duck took all her ducklings to the farmyard.

As soon as the farmyard animals saw the ugly duckling, they began to laugh and shout.

"Most of your ducklings are lovely," clucked the hen. "But look at that big, scruffy, *ugly* one!"

"He's too ugly for this farmyard!" cackled the goose.

The same thing happened the next day, and the day after that. The ducks on the moat and the animals in the farmyard all teased the ugly duckling. Even his own brothers and sisters made fun of him. The ugly duckling had no friends at all.

The ugly duckling was so sad and lonely that he decided to run away, out into the big, wide world.

Early one morning, before anyone else was awake, he ran away, through the reeds, past the moat and the farmyard and the castle walls, till he came to a marsh.

There he saw a flock of wild ducks dabbling in the water.

"What kind of bird are you?" they asked.

"I'm a duckling," the ugly duckling replied.

"No, you're not," said the biggest duck. "You're much too ugly! We don't want to have anything to do with you!" And they turned away, leaving him alone.

The ugly duckling spent two lonely days on the marsh, until a group of hunters came, scaring all the ducks away.

The frightened ugly duckling ran over fields and meadows. He wandered far and wide until he came to a lake where he could swim and find food. There were other ducks there, but when they saw how ugly he was, they kept far away from him.

The ugly duckling stayed on the lake all summer. Then the autumn came, and the weather began to grow cold. All the other ducks began to fly south, where the weather was warmer. The ugly duckling shivered by himself in the tall grass beside the lake.

One evening, just before sunset, the ugly duckling looked up and saw a flock of big, beautiful birds above him. Their white feathers gleamed and they had long, graceful necks. They were flying south, just like the ducks.

The ugly duckling stretched his neck to watch them.

"I wish I could go with them," he thought.

Autumn turned to winter, and the lake froze solid. The ugly duckling couldn't swim any longer. His feathers were caked with ice and snow, and he couldn't find any food.

Luckily, a farmer found the ugly duckling and took him home. The farmer's wife warmed the ugly duckling up by the stove, and the farmer's children tried to play with him. But they were loud and rough.

The ugly duckling was frightened. He flapped his wings and knocked over a milk pail. The farmer's wife chased him out of the house.

Somehow, the ugly duckling found his way to a swamp, and there he managed to live for the rest of the long, hard winter.

When spring came, the ugly duckling found his wings had grown bigger and stronger. He flew across the fields to a canal. There, he saw the beautiful birds he had seen last autumn.

"Hello!" they said.

The ugly duckling looked around. He couldn't believe they were talking to him!

"We are swans," explained one of the birds. "And so are you – you are a very fine young swan indeed!"

The ugly duckling looked down at his reflection in the water. It was true – a handsome swan looked back at him!

The other swans made a circle around him and nuzzled him with their beaks. "Welcome," they said. "We would be happy to have you in our flock!"

The new young swan thought his heart would burst.

"I never dreamed I could be so happy," he thought, "when I was a little ugly duckling."

And, looking around at his new friends, he knew that he would be happy forever.

Dolphin Finds a Star

One night in the moonlight, a baby dolphin called Splash looked up and saw a shooting star. It zoomed across the sky and disappeared.

"That star has fallen into the water!" Splash cried. "I'm going to find it and give it to my mummy as a present. She loves shiny things."

In the distance Splash saw something sparkling. He swam towards the sparkles, thinking it was the star.

But when he got closer, he saw that it was a shoal of flashing fish, wiggling and weaving through the water.

Then Splash saw something glowing above his head. "There's the star! My mummy will be so pleased," he thought happily, and he swam towards the shining light.

But when he got closer, Splash found that the light was a lamp shining on the very top of a sailing boat.

The more the baby dolphin swam around, the more shiny creatures he saw. There were flashing fish, jiggly jellyfish and even sparkly seahorses, but the fallen star was nowhere to be found.

At last, Splash saw a light that was much brighter than all the rest. He swam towards it, hoping it would be the star. He swam through an underwater garden of swirling seaweed and shimmering shells. And then, at last, he found the star. It was in the hair of a beautiful mermaid queen sitting on her throne.

"Hello, baby dolphin. What brings you here?" she asked, but Splash felt very shy. He didn't know what to say.

So the flashing fish, the jiggly jellyfish and the sparkly seahorses all told the mermaid queen:

"He was looking for the star that's in your hair. He wanted to give it to his mummy."

"In that case, you shall have it," said the mermaid, and she handed the shining star to Splash.

Splash gave his mummy the star and she was very pleased.

Together they played with it all day long.

Then, when night came, they jumped up as high as they could and pushed the star back up into the sky, where it could shine down on everyone – on the flashing fish and the jiggly jellyfish, on the sparkly seahorses and on you, too.

The Three Little Pigs

Once upon a time, there were three little pigs. One day, it was time for them to leave home and build houses of their own.

"Watch out for the big bad wolf," warned their mother, as she watched them trot off down the road.

After a while, the three little pigs met a man carrying bundles of straw. So the first little pig bought some and used them to build his very own straw house.

Meanwhile, the second little pig bought a stack of sticks from a woodcutter and began to build a stick house.

The third little pig, who was the smartest of the bunch, bought a load of bricks from a builder and set to work building a fine strong house of bricks.

The next morning, the first little pig was sitting in his straw house when the big bad wolf came along.

"Little pig, let me in!" growled the wolf, peering in.

"Not by the hairs on my chinny chin chin!" replied the piggy.

"Then I'll huff and I'll puff and I'll blow your house down!"

growled the wolf. And that's just what he did.

"Help!" squealed the first little pig, running down the road.

Next, the wolf visited the stick house.

"Little pig, let me in!" he called.

"Not by the hairs on my chinny chin chin!" cried the piggy.

"Then I'll huff and I'll puff and I'll blow your house down!" growled the wolf, and that's exactly what he did.

"Oh, my!" cried the second little pig, running down the road.

When the third little pig saw his brother and sister being chased by the wolf, he quickly let them in and shut the door.

"Little pigs, let me in!" roared the angry wolf.

"Not by the hairs on our chinny chin chins!" cried the pigs.

"Then I'll huff and I'll puff and I'll blow your house down!" cried the wolf. So he huffed and he puffed... but the fine strong house of bricks did not fall down.

"I'm coming down the chimney to gobble you up!" shouted the furious wolf.

As the wolf climbed onto the roof, the three little pigs heaved a big pot of water onto the fire. Then they waited.

WHOOSH! The wolf slid down the chimney and landed with a splash in the boiling water.

"YOUCH!" he howled. And he raced out of the kitchen as fast as his paws would carry him – never to be seen again!

The Dragon Who Was Scared of Flying

Once upon a time, in a land far away, there lived a dragon named Dennis who was scared of flying.

Every day his friends would set off to have adventures, leaving poor Dennis behind on his own. And every evening, the other dragons would return to their caves on the mountain with amazing tales of what they had been up to that day.

"I rescued a damsel in distress," one would say.

"I fought the evil one-eyed giant and won," boasted another.

One day, Dennis could stand it no longer. Instead of retreating into his cave, he set off down the mountainside. It was very tiring having to walk.

Dennis was about to have a rest when he saw some brightly coloured tents in the distance.

"I might take a closer look," thought Dennis. "Maybe I can have an adventure, too!"

When Dennis reached the tents he found himself in a world more exotic than he could ever have imagined. There were acrobats and tightrope walkers and trapeze artists, horses and clowns and a very fat ringmaster in a red coat. In such an incredible place no one gave Dennis a second look. They just assumed he was part of the show!

The only person who knew for sure that Dennis wasn't part of the circus was Claude the ringmaster – because he owned it!

"Hello, there!" he said. "Welcome to Claude's Circus. How do you do?"

"I'm Dennis the dragon," said Dennis.

"A dragon, eh?" said Claude. "Might be quite a crowd-puller! Would you like to join us?"

So Dennis joined the circus. Soon he was the circus's champion fire-eater. Folk would come from far and near to see Dennis shooting flames high into the dark roof of the big top.

One evening, when Dennis had finished his act, he sat watching Carlotta, the tightrope walker, pirouetting high up on the rope as usual. All at once she lost her footing. Dennis saw to his horror that she was going to fall. Without thinking, he flapped his wings furiously – and found himself flying up towards her. He caught her and flew down to the ground. The crowd burst into applause. They obviously thought it was all part of the act.

"Thank you, Dennis," whispered Carlotta. "You saved my life."

Dennis was overjoyed. Not only had he saved Carlotta's life, he had also learned to fly. And, he said with a grin, "I do declare that flying is actually rather fun."

Baby Bear

Brett was a baby bear cub who just couldn't wait to grow up into a big bear.

"I wish I was big and strong like Daddy," he told Mummy Bear one morning. "Then I could leave home and look after myself, just like a grown-up bear."

Mummy Bear smiled and ruffled Brett's furry little head.

"Don't be in such a hurry to grow up," she whispered. "You're my beautiful baby, and I love taking care of you."

"I'm not a baby," cried Brett. "I'm a big bear!"

And to show Mummy just how big he was, he leapt into the river and splashed around until, after a bit of a fight, he managed to catch a tiny, wriggling fish in his mouth.

"See," he cried triumphantly, proudly showing Mummy Bear what he had caught. "I can catch fish like a big grown-up bear."

"Well done," cried Mummy. Then she dipped a large paw into a pool and flipped out a huge fish.

"Oooh," gulped Little Bear. "I guess I've still got a bit to learn about fishing."

Mummy and Brett sat down beside the river and began to gnaw on their fish.

Suddenly, a large eagle began circling above them. He had a huge, curved beak, and razor-sharp claws.

Brett leapt to his feet and began waving his paws around wildly.

"Go away, you big brute!" he bellowed at the top of his voice. The eagle ignored him and prepared to dive.

Mummy Bear lifted up her head and gave a gentle growl. The eagle took one look at her sharp teeth and long claws and soared back up into the sky

"Oooh," gulped Little Bear. "I guess I've got a bit to learn about scaring eagles."

Mummy Bear smiled kindly. Then she picked up Brett and gave him a big, hairy hug.

"There's plenty of time to grow up. You should enjoy being my baby bear first."

"Yes," agreed Brett, snuggling up to his Mummy's warm, soft fur. "Being your baby is kind of nice, after all!"

The Elves and the Shoemaker

Once upon a time there was a kind old shoemaker. He worked hard, but the day came when he had only a few pennies left – just enough to buy leather for one final pair of shoes.

That evening the shoemaker cut up the leather. Then, leaving it on his workbench, he climbed the stairs to bed.

The next morning the shoemaker couldn't believe his eyes. On his workbench was the finest pair of shoes he had ever seen. He put the shoes in his shop window and that afternoon a fine gentleman bought them for a price that amazed the shoemaker.

The money was enough to buy enough leather to make two new pairs of shoes. The shoemaker cut up the leather and left it lying on his workbench. "I'll finish the shoes tomorrow," he yawned, and went to bed.

The next morning, when he came downstairs, the shoemaker saw two fine pairs of beautiful new shoes!

So it went on for weeks. Every night the shoemaker cut out the leather and left it on his workbench, and every morning there were splendid shoes waiting to be sold.

One night the shoemaker and his wife decided that they had to solve the mystery. So, after the shoemaker left the leather on his workbench, they shut up shop and hid in a cupboard.

When the clock struck midnight, two tiny elves appeared. They ran over to the workbench and began to stitch and sew, until they had made five pairs of shoes. Then they shot up the chimney.

"The elves must be frozen in those thin, tattered clothes," said the shoemaker. "And their feet are bare, although they make such beautiful shoes!"

So the shoemaker's wife made two little jackets and two pairs of trousers. The shoemaker made two pairs of tiny boots, fastened with shiny silver buckles. The next evening, they wrapped the little clothes in tissue paper and left them on the workbench. Then they hid in the cupboard and waited.

At the stroke of midnight, the elves appeared. When they opened the presents, they were overjoyed. They put on their new clothes and danced happily all around the shop, singing,

"*See what handsome boys we are!*
We will work on shoes no more!"

Then they flew up the chimney and were gone, never to return again! But the shoemaker and his wife never forgot them.

Little Red Riding Hood

Once upon a time a little girl lived with her mother on the edge of a forest. The little girl always wore a red cloak with a hood, so everyone called her Little Red Riding Hood.

One day, Little Red Riding Hood's mother asked her to take some food to her grandma on the other side of the forest. "Grandma isn't well," she explained. "So be sure to get there quickly and don't speak to any strangers along the way."

Little Red Riding hadn't gone very far when she met a wolf.

"Hello," purred the wolf. "Where are you going?"

"To see my sick grandma on the other side of the forest," replied Little Red Riding Hood, who had forgotten her mother's warning.

"Oh, really," said the wolf. And without saying another word, he dashed off.

The wolf didn't stop until he reached Grandma's house. He raced into her bedroom and gobbled her up. Then he put on her nightgown and climbed into her bed.

Soon Little Red Riding Hood arrived.

"Where are you, Grandma?" she called.

"I'm in bed," croaked the wolf.

"How strange she sounds," thought Little
Red Riding Hood.
But when she entered
the bedroom she gulped
in surprise.

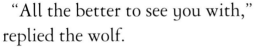

"What big eyes you
have, Grandma," she
said.

"All the better to see you with,"
replied the wolf.

"What big ears you have," said Little Red Riding Hood.

"All the better to hear you with," said the wolf.

"What big teeth you have," spluttered the little girl.

"All the better to eat you with," roared the wolf, leaping up.

"Help!" screamed Little Red Riding Hood, as the wolf
gobbled her down in one gulp!

Her screams were so loud that a passing woodcutter rushed in
to see what was going on. When he saw the wolf's big belly,
he picked him up and shook him. The wolf gave a loud burp
and out shot Little Red Riding Hood, followed by Grandma.

They were rather rumpled and crumpled and very, very
annoyed. The wolf took one look at their angry faces, and the
woodcutter's axe, and raced away.

From that day on, the wolf never dared enter the forest, and
Little Red Riding Hood never spoke to strangers ever again.

Mythical Monster

The monster lay in the mud at the bottom of the lake. She was sad. Everything had changed. Once, she'd been the most famous monster in the world. But now only a few people bothered to stand around waiting for a glimpse of her.

The monster knew what had gone wrong: she'd been too mean with her appearances. Once every twenty years just wasn't enough. People had got bored waiting.

She knew what to do. She had to make a splash! She swam across the lake, her spotted back breaking the surface. But when she lifted her neck, she saw that the shore was empty. In the distance there was a campsite, but the people there weren't looking towards the lake. They were outside their tents, reading newspapers and cooking supper. No one was interested in her.

She'd have to show herself properly, she decided. She swam to the shore and lumbered into the middle of the campsite.

A woman walked out of a tent. "Hey kids, that's a great costume," she cried, when she saw the monster. "Wherever did you get it? Now have a wash. Supper'll be ready soon."

As the monster was walking sadly back to the lake, a boy

came along. He screamed. "It's the monster!" he shouted.

"I wouldn't bother yourself with all that," said the monster to the astonished boy. "No one believes in me any more."

"That's terrible," said the boy. "We'll have to think of something that will get people's attention. I know – why don't I row out onto the lake and then pretend to be in trouble. Then you can rescue me."

The boy rowed himself out onto the lake, then deliberately pushed the oars away. "Help! I'm going to drown!" he cried.

The campers came running to the shore. Right on cue, the monster reared up out of the water. A great wave engulfed the boat, tossing the boy into the water.

"The monster's attacking my son!" cried a woman.

"That isn't what I had in mind," thought the monster. She plucked the boy from the water with her huge jaws.

"It's eating my son!" cried the woman.

Holding the boy in her mouth, the monster swam to the shore and put him down in front of his mother.

"The monster's saved my son!" cried the woman. "It's a hero!"

Cameras were flashing everywhere. "That's enough for me," the monster thought. She dived to the bottom of the lake. "I'll lay low for a while," she said to herself. "Just for another twenty years or so. A monster can only take so much attention, after all."

Chicken Licken

Chicken Licken was a little brown hen who lived on a farm with lots of other animals. Every day she sat under a big oak tree to take an afternoon nap. One day she was resting there when a big acorn fell down and landed with a loud bump on her head.

"Ouch!" said Chicken Licken, rubbing her head with her wing. **"The sky is falling!** I must tell the king. He will know what to do."

So Chicken Licken set off to see the king. On the way she met Cocky Locky.

"Where are you going?" he asked.

"I am going to see the king," replied Chicken Licken. **"The sky is falling!** He will know what to do."

"Then I will come with you," said Cocky Locky.

So Chicken Licken and Cocky Locky ran on. On the way, they met Ducky Lucky.

"We are going to see the king," said Chicken Licken. **"The sky is falling!** He will know what to do about it."

"Then I will come with you," said Ducky Lucky.

So Chicken Licken, Cocky Locky and Ducky Lucky ran on.

On the way, they met Goosey Loosey.

"Where are you going?" asked Goosey Loosey.

"We are going to see the king," said Chicken Licken. **"The sky is falling!** He will know what to do."

"Then I will come with you," said Goosey Loosey.

So Chicken Licken, Cocky Locky, Ducky Lucky and Goosey Loosey ran on.

On the way, they met Foxy Loxy, who was going for a stroll.

"Where are you going?" asked Foxy Loxy.

"We are going to see the king," said Chicken Licken. **"The sky is falling!** He will know what to do."

"Oh, dear," said Foxy Loxy, with a wicked glint in his eye, licking his lips. "I do believe you are going the wrong way."

"Goodness!" squawked Chicken Licken, getting in a flap.
"Whatever shall we do? We must speak to the king as soon
as possible."

"Then follow me!" said Foxy Loxy slyly. "I will show you the
quickest way to go."

So Chicken Licken, Cocky Locky, Ducky Lucky and Goosey
Loosey went on and on, following in Foxy Loxy's footsteps.

"Where are we going?" asked Chicken Licken. "Are we nearly
there yet?"

Foxy Loxy smiled. "Just keep on following," he said.

Finally they arrived at a dark cave in the hillside.

"You must come in here!" said Foxy Loxy, leading the way
into the cave. "This is a short cut. I am the only creature that
knows about it. You will reach the king much more quickly
if you come this way."

So Chicken Licken, Cocky
Locky, Ducky Lucky and
Goosey Loosey followed
Foxy Loxy inside.

But oh, dearie me! It wasn't a short cut at all. It wasn't even a secret passageway. It was Foxy Loxy's den, and that crafty creature had dinner on his mind.

"**I'm hungry!**" he growled. "And now I am going to gobble you all up."

"Cock-a-doodle-do! Run for your lives!" cried Cocky Locky, as Foxy Loxy opened his jaws wide.

"Oh, no!" cried Chicken Licken, Ducky Lucky and Goosey Loosey, flapping their wings in alarm. "Run away! Run away!"

And that's exactly what those silly birds did – as fast as their legs would carry them. And they didn't stop running until they were home.

And as for Chicken Licken? She never did tell the king that the sky was falling down. Which is just as well, really.